These poem

From

Published by:
Candlestick Press, Diversity House, 72 Nottingham Road,
Arnold, Nottingham NG5 6LF

www.candlestickpress.co.uk

Printed by Ratcliff & Roper Print Group, Nottinghamshire, UK

Reprinted 2016

ISBN 978 1 907598 23 4

Acknowledgements:
Our thanks to Kit Wright for permission to reproduce 'The Head's Hideout' from *Cat Among the Pigeons: Poems* (Viking Kestrel 1987, Puffin Books 1989). 'Please Mrs Butler' by Allan Ahlberg is from *Please Mrs Butler*, (Kestrel 1983, Puffin Books 1984) Copyright © Allan Ahlberg, 1983. Reproduced by permission of Penguin Books Ltd. 'One day while we were getting out our rough books' by John Hegley is from *Can I Come Down Now, Dad?* (Mandarin, 1997).

A Teacher from Leeds

There once was a teacher from Leeds

Who swallowed a packet of seeds.

In less than an hour

Her nose was a flower

And her hair was a posy of weeds.

Anon

The Head's Hideout

The Head crouched in his hideout

Beneath a dustbin lid.

"I want to see," he muttered,

"No teacher and no kid,

“No parent, no inspector,

Never a district nurse,

And, please, not one school dinner:

The things are getting worse!”

All morning, as the phone rang,

He hid away. Instead:

“The Head is in the dustbin,”

The secretary said.

"The *Head* is in the *dustbin*?"

"Yes, he'll be there all day.

He likes sometimes to manage

A little getaway.

"Last year he went to Holland.

Next year he's off to France.

Today he's in the dustbin.

You have to take your chance."

The Head sprang from the garbage

As end-of-school came round.

He cried, "That's quite the nastiest

Hideaway I've found!

"I think I'll stick to teachers

And kids and parents too.

It's just sometimes I've had enough."

Don't blame him. Do you?

Kit Wright

One day while we were getting out our rough books

one day while we were getting out our rough books

there was a bit of a chattering

and Miss went all red and said stop stop stop

STOP STOP STOP

and we were very quiet

and Miss went more red and said

there is something the matter with the children

in class two purple

do you know what you are?

DO YOU KNOW WHAT YOU ARE?

and we were very very frightened

and we did not know what we were

John Hegley

Snow in Schooltime

All Saturday the sky was clear,
But now again that Monday's here
It snows; and through the window glass
We see the flying snowflakes pass.

The teacher never seems to know
The fun it is to have the snow;
She thinks that we can sit and think,
And write long words with pen and ink,

And listen well to three times three,
And be as quiet as can be,
And never once peep out around
To see how much stays on the ground.

Annette Wynne

3×3 = SNOW
3×4 = SNOW

Please Mrs Butler

Please Mrs Butler

This boy Derek Drew

Keeps copying my work, Miss.

What shall I do?

Go and sit in the hall, dear.

Go and sit in the sink.

Take your books on the roof, my lamb.

Do whatever you think.

Please Mrs Butler

This boy Derek Drew

Keeps taking my rubber, Miss.

What shall I do?

Keep it in your hand, dear.

Hide it up your vest.

Swallow it if you like, my love.

Do what you think best.

Please Mrs Butler

This boy Derek Drew

Keeps calling me rude names, Miss.

What shall I do?

Lock yourself in the cupboard, dear.

Run away to sea.

Do whatever you can, my flower.

But don't ask me!

Allan Ahlberg

Now it's your turn to write a poem about your teachers or draw a picture of them!